Best of

AKBAR
BIRBAL

Best of
AKBAR
BIRBAL'S

TINY TOT PUBLICATIONS
INDIA

Best of
Akbar-Birbal's

© 2002 TINY TOT PUBLICATIONS
This Edition:-2002

Retold & Edited by: Shyam Dua

Published By:
TINY TOT PUBLICATIONS
235, Jagriti Enclave,
Vikas marg,
Delhi-110092 (INDIA)
Ph.: 216 7314, 216 3582,
Fax:- 91-11-2373023
email: tinytotpub@indiatimes.com

ISBN 81-7573-574-0

Illustrated by
Aakriti Features, Delhi

Printed at : HAPLOOS New Delhi Ph. : 549 8686

The Dead Parrot's Tale

One fine morning, Akbar's favoured servant arrived at Birbal's doorstep. He was very worried and nearly in tears.

"What's the matter, Ali ?" Birbal enquired. "Sir, my life is in danger. Only you can help me out," Ali replied.

"I'll do my best but first tell me what's wrong ?"

"Sir, a few months ago, a fakir had given a parrot to His Majesty. He had handed me that parrot and asked me to take good care of it. He ordered that anyone who would bring the news of its death would be sentenced to death. Sir, inspite of the best care and attention, I found the parrot lying dead in the cage this morning. Now I fear for my life."

"Is that all ? Don't fear for it. You go home and leave it to me. I'll give this news to His Majesty and still have my life spared." Ali went home reassured.

Birbal went to Akbar's court and said, "Your Majesty,

the parrot gifted to you by the fakir is a holy spirit indeed. I went to see it this morning and found it deep in meditation. He lay on his back, facing skywards with closed eyes."

"Is that so ? You must be joking. Anyway let's go and see," Akbar agreed.

So King Akbar, Birbal and some courtiers went to Ali's house.

"Birbal, truly you are an intelligent man of wit. But there are times when one must stay within limits. I can see that the parrot is dead. Do you think that I am a fool ? Don't pretend that you knew nothing about this."

"Your Majesty, I knew about it but I merely acted this way to save my life."

Akbar then remembered his words when he had asked Ali to look after the parrot.

He called Ali and then addressed Birbal, "Birbal, you have once again saved a life by your wit. Now I know why you did this."

Thus, Ali was forgiven and Birbal was thanked profusely by him.

A Pot Full of Intelligence

One day a messenger arrived in Akbar's court from Sri Lanka. He had a strange request indeed. He said, "Your Majesty, the whole world knows about the intelligent and learned courtiers that adorn your court. The king of Sri Lanka has sent me here to get a pot full of intelligence."

Suddenly the court was filled with whispers, "A pot full of intelligence, so weird !" "The Sri Lankan King wants to make a fool of us!" "I don't think we can fulfil this request at all." Just then Birbal got up and said, "Your Majesty, we can arrange a pot full of intelligence but we need some weeks to do so."

The messenger replied, "Oh, time is no concern for us. I can wait for some weeks."

Birbal went home and called his servant. "Get some small mouthed

earthen pots for me." Within few minutes, the servant came back with a dozen such pots. Birbal and the servant went to the place where many pumpkins had been planted. Birbal took the pots and placed the plant's flower inside the mouths of the pots. Then he gave instructions to the servant that the pots must not be removed till instructed.

A few days later, Akbar enquired about the pots of intelligence. Birbal told him, "Your Majesty, it will take a few weeks more and the pot will be filled to the top with intelligence." A fortnight later, Birbal went to check the pumpkin plants. He saw that the pumpkins had grown to the size of the pots. He called the servant and asked him to remove the pots full of pumpkins carefully.

Next morning, in Akbar's court, he called upon the Sri Lankan king's messenger, "Sir, I present you a pot full of intelligence." Birbal's servant stepped forward with an earthen pot whose mouth was covered with a cloth. The messenger took the pot.

Birbal said, "Sir, being a most valuable thing, we keep the intelligence in precious pots. So, I request you to empty the pot and return it without a scratch on it. The fruit of intelligence will be effective only if removed without damaging it."

At this the messenger looked inside the pot. He was taken aback. Birbal continued, "If the king of Sri Lanka wishes for more intelligence. I have about ten more of such pots."

The messenger thought that he had surely been outwitted by Birbal. His King should not have challenged Akbar courtiers. The messenger left without a word and took the pot with him.

Then King Akbar requested to see the pot of intelligence for himself. Soon Birbal

sent for them. The servant arrived with ten more such pots. King Akbar peeped into one of them and burst out laughing on seeing the pumpkin, "Oh, surely Birbal has gifted the King of Sri Lanka enough intelligence to last a lifetime."

The Sweet Truth

Birbal's neighbour, Karim was crazy about knowing his future. He often had invited fortune-tellers and palmists to know what the future held for him.

One morning as Birbal was strolling in his garden he heard Karim's loud voice, "Go away, you cheat. You know nothing about fortune-telling. Don't try to come this way again."

Birbal saw that Karim was pushing a fortune-teller out of his gate. Birbal went to the fortune-teller and asked, "What did you say to make Karim angry ?" "Sir, I merely looked at his palm and told him that all his relatives would die before him and then......"

"Ah ! Then he pushed you out."

"Yes Sir. I guess he could not digest the bitter truth but I do not and cannot lie about such things."

"Oh ! You are honest and truthful and that's **a good** quality indeed. But you know that truth is always bitter. You must now offer him 'sweet' truth."

"Sweet truth ! How do I do that ?"

"Here's how," said Birbal and whispered a plan in the fortune-teller's ears.

Next day, the fortune-teller disguised himself as an old man. He approached Karim's doorstep. Karim saw him and came out. The fortune-teller exclaimed, "Oh sir ! What grand personality you have. Can I read your palm, please ?"

"Oh yes, please do come inside," Karim replied.

The fortune-teller studied Karim's palm and said, "What great fortunes you have ! You have a very long and prosperous life ahead of you. In fact, you will certainly outlive all your friends and relatives."

"Is that true? And that foolish fortune-teller yesterday said,...... Oh ! Let him be. I am so happy to hear what you told me. Please feel free to pay more visits in the future."

Then Karim went in and returned with a bag full of gold coins. "Please accept this from my side. Do visit me sometime. I'll eagerly look forward to it."

The fortune-teller took the gold coins and went away happily. He went to Birbal and said, "Oh, Sir ! I really didn't know that more than the truth, it's how you present it that counts !"

The Royal Touch

One day an old woman and her widow daughter-in-law arrived at Birbal's doorstep. The old woman said to him, "Sir, my son has passed away recently. He had been a soldier in the royal army for the last two decades. After his death, we are in trouble. Please help us out."

"Oh, don't worry about that," Birbal said. "Our king, Akbar, is very just and merciful. Just do what I say and you'll get your dues."

Next morning both the woman and her daughter-in-law presented themselves in the royal court. The old woman had an old sword in her hand. Raising it up, she said to Akbar, "Your Majesty, my son has fought many a battles with this sword. Please keep it

in your armoury."

The king took the sword and examined it. He said, "This is an old rusty sword and it's of no use to us." Handing it to a servant, he said, "Give it back to the old woman with five gold coins."

Birbal was taken aback. He said, "Your Majesty, may I see the sword." Taking it from the hand of the King, he examined the sword closely. King Akbar enquired, "What's the matter, Birbal?"

"Your Majesty, I am sure that once this rusty old sword would receive the royal touch, it would surely turn to gold. I wonder why your merciful hands have had no effect on it."

King Akbar understood what Birbal was trying to say. So he ordered his servant, "Weigh the sword and give the gold coins to the old woman equal in weight to the sword."

The two women thanked King Akbar and blessed Birbal before leaving the court.

The Exact Image

One evening, as Birbal was strolling in the royal garden, he saw that the cheerful natured royal painter was standing in a pensive mood. Birbal was taken aback.

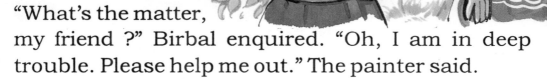

"What's the matter, my friend ?" Birbal enquired. "Oh, I am in deep trouble. Please help me out." The painter said.

"Yes, do tell me if I can help you."

The painter took Birbal to his mansion and showed him five pictures, all of the same person.

"These are all pictures of Amir Sardar. He challenged me to paint his exact image and I agreed. After sitting for the first painting one full day, I told him that I would return tomorrow after giving it the finishing touches.

Next morning I showed him the picture but it was not his exact image. The day before he had a beard but that morning he had only moustache. I again painted his picture and left it to give it the finishing touches the next day. I returned the next morning. After giving the finishing touches, I showed him the picture again. This time, too it was not exact because cunning Amir had shaved off his moustache. His painting had a moustache he had sported the day before. Three more times he made some changes to trouble me. Now I have wasted so much time and effort with no use. My art and talent is being questioned."

"Oh, I understand, my friend," said Birbal. "Just follow my advice

and Amir Sardar will trouble you no more."

The next day the royal painter went to Amir Sardar's mansion. "Sir, here's your exact image." Said the painter. Amir opened the package and saw his face reflected in a mirror. "You cheat ! How dare you take me for a fool. This is no picture of mine. This is a mirror !"

Just then Birbal arrived and said, "Yes Amir ! This is your exact image, just as you wished for !"

Amir Sardar agreed that he was defeated and paid money to the royal painter. Once more Birbal saw that the royal painter was his cheerful self.

A Widow's Fortune

One day an old widow went to Birbal with her tale of woe. She said, "Sir, I've been tricked. Please do justice."

"Tricked, by whom ?" enquired Birbal.

The widow told Birbal, "Sir, six months ago I decided to go on the pilgrimage. But I didn't know what to do with my savings. I wanted to keep them safe. So I went to a sage and said, "I am going on a pilgrimage. I have some copper coins in this bag. They are all my savings. Please keep them with you till I return from my pilgrimage."

"At this, the sage said, "I am sorry, I am above all materialistic pleasures of life. So I will not touch your money. Dig a hole in any corner of my hut and hide this bag there."

"I did so and went away reassured. When I

returned from my pilgrimage, I went to the sage's hut to get my bag back. I dug the place where I had hidden the bag But, unfortunately, I found there nothing. I went to the sage to claim my savings. The sage said, "I do not know where you had hid your money. I have told you earlier that I don't touch money. Please dig it out from wherever you had hidden it."

"I am sure that the sage is a cheat but he is not confessing to the theft. Please, do help me get my copper coins."

Birbal thought for a while and told about his plan to the old widow.

Next day Birbal went to the sage's hut with a small silver box in his hands and said,

"O learned one, I have heard much about you, and today I have the honour of meeting you. I need your help but I don't know what to say...."

As Birbal continued, the sage kept eyeing the silver box in his hands, "Oh ! What does he have in that small box !" he wondered.

"O learned one," Birbal continued, "I know you are no longer concerned with worldly affairs and material goods hold no attraction to you. But, in this world of greedy people, I can only trust you." Birbal opened the silver box and said, "Could you keep this box full of precious gems for me ? I have to go to Ajmer to meet my brother."

"Oh, son, I will not touch these worldly goods at all. Just dig a hole in any corner of my hut and hide your box in it."

Just as Birbal was to do so, the sage saw the old

widow at the doorstep. He thought, "Oh, this old woman has come to spoil the show. I must return her copper coins. After all, what are they before these precious gems ?" Thinking so, the sage said aloud, "Oh, I am so glad you are here. I think you had forgotten in which corner you had hidden your wealth. Go in the northern corner and look for your bag. Maybe it's there."

The old widow found her coins where the sage had hidden them. She went away happily holding her bag of coins close to her heart. Just then Birbal's servant arrived there and said, "Sir, come home soon. Your brother is here from Ajmer to meet you."

"Oh, is that so !" Birbal turned to the sage and said, "O learned one, you do not have to trouble yourself with my wealth. My brother is here so I won't need to leave the box in your care."

Then Birbal left with his box and was happy at his successful plan. The sage realized that his greed had left him with nothing at all.

(21)

Who is the Greatest ?

As usual, King Akbar was in the mood of asking questions. He asked a courtier a question, "Tell me, who is the greatest Lord-Indra or me ?"

"Lord, Indra, Your majesty," immediately came the reply.

"How dare you say that ?" King Akbar got angry. He asked the next courtier, "Who is greatest Lord-Indra or me ?"

"You are greater than him. In fact you are the greatest, Your Majesty," the second courtier said. "Well, then prove it to me," the King challenged.

Just when the courtier was getting nervous at the challenge, Birbal entered the court. He had heard what had happened. He offered, "It is very easy to prove, Your Majesty. In fact even Lord Brahma faced this dilemma. He had ordered two idols to be made, one of yours and the other of Lord Indra. Then the idols were placed in the heavenly scale to see which was larger and greater. As your idol was

heavier, the idol came towards the Earth, but as Lord Indra's idol was light, he went up towards Heaven. So it is that he rules Heaven and you are the Emperor of the Earth."

King Akbar was impressed by Birbal's words and burst out laughing.

Fields of Pearls

One day King Akbar's Queen was walking past, when her hand accidentally knocked down a vase.

"Oh," she exclaimed. "This was His Majesty's favourite vase. I can't tell him that it is broken."

A little later, the King entered his chamber. He found something amiss and remembered that he could not see the vase. He asked the Queen, "Dear, where's that vase which was gifted to me by a Chinese traveller ?"

"Oh, Your majesty, the servant has taken it to wipe off the dust from it," the Queen lied.

Later on when the King awakened in the morning and was feeling fresh and relaxed, the Queen confessed, "Your Majesty, I lied to you about the vase. I knocked it down accidentally and it broke into pieces."

"But you said the servant had taken to clean it. You

are King Akbar's Queen yet you dared to lie before me. I forgive you for breaking the vase as it was an accident. But I'll not forgive you for being a liar. I order you to leave the royal palace immediately."

Inspite of many pleas, the King did not relent. She went away to the palace just outside Agra. Soon everyone knew that the Queen had left the royal palace.

Next morning in the royal court the King asked, "Has anyone ever lied ?"

All the courtiers feared for their lives so all of them answered that they had always spoken the truth. Just then Birbal came to the court. He had been away from Agra and returned that morning. He was posed the same question. Birbal replied, "I tried to be honest all the while but once in a while there are times one has to take help of small lies."

"So you are telling me that you have been dishonest. But all the courtiers present here have not lied even once in their lives."

Birbal knew all of them were lying. Akbar became angry and said, "Birbal, I do not want a lying minister in my court. I order you to leave Agra immediately."

Soon this news reached the Queen's palace on

the outskirts of Agra. She asked her maid to fetch Birbal in her presence. When Birbal and the Queen met, she told him what had happened before. Birbal promised to help her.

Birbal went to the best jeweller of the town. He showed him a corn of wheat and said, "I want you to take the best pearls and make such identical corns of pearls."

Within a few days the corns of pearls were ready. Birbal went to King Akbar's court. After taking permission to enter, he met the King and said, "Your Majesty, on the way out of the city, I met a traveller. He gave me these extra-ordinary corns of pearls. If we are to sow them, we can have fields of pearls."

Akbar was amazed to see the corns of pearls. He said, "Is it truly possible ?"

"Well, at least we can try. I have found a piece of fertile land. Next week on full moon night we must sow these corns," Birbal said.

The King agreed. Soon the news spread and a large crowd gathered at the site on the decided night.

"Now Birbal, start sowing the corn of pearls," the

King said.

"Oh no your Majesty. I can't sow them as I have lied in my life. Only one, who has never sinned, who is pure and has never lied, can sow the corn. I can't do this but surely any of your truthful courtier can," Birbal replied.

The courtiers were taken aback. They knew they were liars and may be the pearls would not sprout if they sowed them. Every one of them refused. So Birbal said, "Your Majesty, you are the only truthful person present here. You can sow the corns of pearls."

"Birbal, I can't sow them because I am sure I must have lied at many times as a kid. I am afraid we cannot find anyone who has never lied in his life."

Then King Akbar realized the importance of what he had just said. He forgave Birbal and the Queen and ordered both of them to return to Agra.

Yakin Shah's Monument

It was King Akbar's birthday. On that day, every year many kings and ministers visited his royal court to wish him. Along with them came many Brahmins, Fakirs and mahatmas. The King was placed in a scale and food and coconuts, hundred times his weight were given away to them. As they blessed the King, Birbal watched them. He thought to himself, "His Majesty is so pure of heart. He can't make out that most of them are imposters who have come only for the alms he is giving away. The King believes in them and gets influenced by them easily."

As he smiled to himself, King Akbar saw Birbal. Later on King Akbar enquired, "Birbal, the miracles that Brahmins, fakirs and mahatmas do are great. Do you think they are due to the learned men's powers or the belief of the followers ?"

"I think it's purely blind faith that does it, Your Majesty," Birbal replied.

"But aren't these great men the messengers who carry our words to God ?"

"No, Your Majesty, it's our faith that makes them the honoured men."

"Oh ! I think you are insulting them by saying such words," King Akbar said angrily.

"No, Your Majesty. I am a Hindu. All Hindus are idol worshippers. It's our belief in the idol that makes our prayers come true and not the idol itself."

"Oh, you are being derogatory. But I think you must be given a chance to prove your words. You have a month to do or you'll be sentenced to death."

Birbal accepted the challenge. He went out of Agra. At the outskirts of the city, he saw a deserted land area. He ordered some masons to make a monument there. When the monument was built, Birbal asked his servants to go around spreading

words about Yakin Shah's monument. In Urdu, 'Yakin' means 'belief'. Soon the servants made up some stories about miracles performed by Yakin Shah whose monument had been built recently. In a few days, crowds thronged the monument to wish for miracle cures and solving of other such problems.

The tales of Yakin Shah soon reached King Akbar's ears. He, too, paid a visit to the monument. Birbal and other courtiers accompanied him. At the monument, there was already a large crowd waiting to offer prayers. King Akbar approached the monument and bowed in reverence. Everyone else did the same except Birbal.

"Why aren't you paying regards, Birbal ?"

"I'll only do that when you'll agree that belief is greater than fakirs and mahatmas," replied Birbal.

King Akbar did not pay heed. He bowed his head and wished that Rana Pratap of Mewar must be defeated in the battle that was being fought by

Prince Salim. A few minutes later a soldier on horse back brought the news of Rana's defeat.

King Akbar was overjoyed. He turned to Birbal and said, "Do you see how Yakin Shah has fulfilled my wish ? What more do you want as proof ?"

"No, Your Majesty," Birbal disagreed. "It's your belief in Yakin Shah that has fulfilled the wish."

At this King Akbar got very irritated. "Birbal, your one month time to prove your words is over. Now you must prepare to die."

At this Birbal blurted out,

"Oh Yakin Shah! If you save my life, I'll build a marble memorial for you."

"Oh, Birbal, think about what you are saying," laughed the King. But then Birbal swept away the carpet of flowers from the site of the monument and put his hand in a gap there. Then he pulled out a bundle. It was King Akbar's Pashmina shawl. While opening the bundle of Pashmina shawl, he said, "Your Majesty, here's your Yakin Shah," and then dropped King Akbar's shoe from the shawl's bundle. Birbal continued, "Your Majesty, now tell me are the fakirs and mahatmas or the belief in them that fulfills our wishes ?"

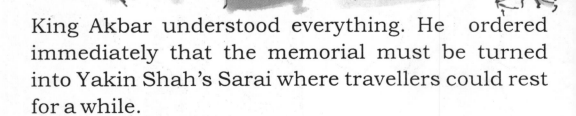

King Akbar understood everything. He ordered immediately that the memorial must be turned into Yakin Shah's Sarai where travellers could rest for a while.

Why God Helps us Himself ?

One day King Akbar asked Birbal, "Why is it that Hindu Gods behave so strangely ?"

Birbal thought, "Our King respects Hinduism and Islam equally. He must be trying to tease me by asking such a question."

King Akbar continued, "Lord Krishna is a fine example of that. Doesn't your Lord Krishna have any servant? Each time a devotee calls for help, the Lord runs himself to see the devotee's needs. Surely he can employ others to do such work ?"

"Oh yes, surely he can," Birbal replied but he already had a plan to explain the facts to the king.

Birbal knew King Akbar loved his grandson, Khurram, very much. Birbal asked a statue-maker to make a wax idol of Prince Khurram which was his exact image. When the idol was ready, he called Khurram's guardian and said, "Take this idol and dress him up in the Prince's clothes and jewels. Go to the lake in the royal garden with the idol in your hand. At my signal act as if you have slipped. Then let the idol fall in water."

The Prince's guardian agreed. Birbal came into the garden with King Akbar. At Birbal's signal, the guardian dropped the wax idol into the deep lake. As soon as King Akbar saw this, he jumped into the lake's cold water to rescue his grandson. He realized later that it was just a wax idol.

As King Akbar was helped out of the lake by the guardians, Birbal commented, "Your Majesty, why did you jump into the cold lake to rescue young Prince while You have so many guards and servants at your beck and call ?"

"Oh, I have hundreds of them but my grandson is my precious one, so I couldn't stop myself."

"Now, you see, Your Majesty, that's why Lord Krishna, who loves each of his devotees, comes to their help himself."

"As always, I agree with you, Birbal," smiled King Akbar as he walked away.

The Royal Hunt

A group of poor villagers went to Birbal. They told him their problem. "Sir, please do something to prevent our village from being deserted."

"What's wrong with your village, my friends ?" Birbal enquired.

"Sir, King Akbar wants more forests in his kingdom. He has ordered his men to take the land where villages are settled and turn them into forests. More forests would mean more animals for His Majesty to fulfill his hobby of hunting."

"Friends I'll try my best to solve your problem."

The next time when King Akbar went on a hunting trip, Birbal accompanied him. They passed by a tree where some owls were busy making a lot of hooting sounds. A courtier with them teased Birbal, "Sir, you are a learned man. I am sure you can tell what the two groups of owls are fighting about."

"Oh, yes, why not ? But His Majesty won't be happy to know," Birbal said with a smile.

At this, the King said, "Why, Birbal ? I don't mind what mere birds would be talking about."

Birbal said, "One of the male owl from our neighbouring kingdom is to wed a female owl from our kingdom. The male owl's relatives have come here to discuss the dowry. They are demanding at least forty forests as dowry. But the female owl's father is not agreeing to fulfill the demand right now. He has learnt that King Akbar would be turning many villages into forests to get more hunting areas. Soon, when the number of forests would increase, the female owl's father would pass the forests as dowry."

King Akbar realized his mistake and said, "Birbal, I was being selfish in destroying villages to get hunting areas for my own silly hobby. I'll order my men to stop vacating the villages."

Thus, once again Birbal did justice to people who had asked for his help.

The Lime-eating Servant

Once King Akbar saw that the palace wall had its plaster coming off. He called his servant and ordered,

"Jumman, I want this wall to be mended. Get some lime (chuna) and paint it soon. Get to work right now."

"As you wish, Your Majesty," Jumman bowed. The next day King Akbar saw that the wall was not mended. He called Jumman and said, "You fool, you have not mended the wall yet. Go immediately and get a pound of lime right now."

As Jumman ran out in a hurry, he collided with Birbal. On enquiring, Jumman told him what had happened.

"Was the King very angry ?" Birbal asked.

"Yes, sir, he was," Jumman replied.

"Now get two bowls. In one, place some lime and in the other, put what I give you. In his anger the King will surely ask you to eat lime, when he says so, simply eat from the bowl in which I'll give you something." Jumman agreed.

As predicted, the angry King Akbar asked Jumman to eat the lime as a punishment. But Jumman ate from the bowl in which Birbal had placed something else. The King was surprised when Jumman ate up the lime as he had ordered. Then the King said, "Now that's enough. You can go now."

As Jumman left, the King thought, "Poor man, Jumman is going to be ill for weeks after my punishment."

But the next day King Akbar was surprised to see Jumman in good health. He thought to himself, "It means Jumman has good digestion. I'll test him again."

He again ordered Jumman to get some lime. Jumman ran to Birbal for help. Birbal advised him to do the same as the day before. Once again King Akbar asked Jumman to eat the lime but this time from both the bowls. Jumman was prepared already and soon followed the King's order. The next

day King Akbar saw Jumman well and good and busy working. The King called Jumman and asked, "Yesterday why were you late when you went to get the bowls of lime?"

"Your Majesty, I had met Birbal Saheb on the way. He asked me to do a small task. I had been late for this reason."

Then King Akbar asked Jumman to get the lime bowls. As he inspected, he found that it had traces of white butter in it. Birbal had asked Jumman to put white butter in the lime bowls, so that he could eat it easily when the angry King ordered him to. King Akbar marvelled at the great ideas Birbal always had to save the skin of others.

Birbal's Secret

One day as Birbal entered King Akbar's court, he saw all the courtiers laughing and smiling. He asked the King, "Your Majesty, why is everyone in a merry mood ?"

"Oh, nothing particular Birbal," the King replied. "We were discussing the colour of people's skin. Most of the courtiers and even I am a fair complexioned man. How are you darker than us ?"

As always, Birbal had an answer ready, "Oh! I think you do not know the secret behind my complexion of skin."

"Secret, what secret is it ?" enquired the King.

"A long time ago, God created the world full of plants, birds and animals. He was not satisfied with that

creation, so he made his ultimate creation-man. God was very happy to see His new creation. So He decided to gift looks, wealth and brains to all. He announced that every human was given five minutes to gather the gifts they liked. I got busy in collecting brain full of intelligence in wit and had no time left to take the other things. All of you were busy collecting looks and wealth and the rest is history."

Hearing this no one had a suitable retort to make. But King Akbar laughed out loud at Birbal's presence of mind in answering any query.

Birbal, the Detective

The gardener of the royal garden, Kalu, was a hardworking man. He always lived in simple clothes, not spending much as he was a miser, too. Once, when one of his friends asked why he did not spend his money, the gardener replied that he was saving it for his old age. He had kept his money in a secret hidden place.

One fine morning Kalu went crying to Birbal, "Sir, I am ruined. Someone has stolen my life's savings. I had worked hard and saved a thousand gold coins but they are gone."

"Where had you kept them, Kalu ?"

"I had dug a hole under the pear tree in the royal garden and kept my money hidden there."

"But why there ?" enquired Birbal.

"Sir, I work in the royal garden the whole day. I can watch over the money and so it is the safest place to keep the money in."

"I see, but did anyone else know about this place ?"

"No sir, only I knew about it."

"Alright! Give me some time to solve the case."
Then Birbal thought, "One could know about the
money bag only if one dug up under the tree. Yes, I
know what to do now."

Birbal asked all the Vaidyas and Hakims (people
who cure by natural ingredients mixed to make
medicines) to come to his mansion. He posed them
a question, "Does any part of the pear tree serve as
medicine ?"

All of them declined but one of them said, "Pear as
a fruit is very good for health but its flowers and
leaves are of no use for us."

Then an old and experienced Vaidya got up
and said, "Sir, recently I made a

paste of some herbs and mixed it with the paste made of the roots of a pear tree. That I gave to a particularly wealthy patient of mine. His name is Seth Hazarimal and he was suffering from jaundice."

"Oh, now please call Seth Hazarimal."

When the Seth arrived, Birbal enquired, "Did you eat a paste of herbs and roots of pear tree to cure your jaundice ?"

"Yes sir. That is why I am standing before you in good health."

"Who got the roots of the pear tree for you ?" Ask Birbal.

"My servant , Sir." replied the Seth.

"Call your servant immediately."

Seth Hazarimal's servant was summoned. On his arrival, Birbal asked, "Did you dig up the roots of a pear tree ?"

"Yes, sir, I did."

"Where was this tree ?"

"In the royal garden, sir.".

"Did you not take the bag full of gold coins you found there ? Give them to me immediately."

"B-b but ....Sir," stammered the servant.

"Return the gold coins to me so that you will be forgiven or ...."

"Sir, I'll get the gold coins for you," The servant ran off and returned with the gold coins.

"I forgive you, but you must promise never to steal again," said Birbal. "As you have confessed, you can take five gold coins for yourself."

Then Birbal called Kalu and gave him his bag full of gold coins. Birbal said, "Here's your savings. I have

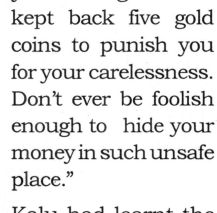

kept back five gold coins to punish you for your carelessness. Don't ever be foolish enough to hide your money in such unsafe place."

Kalu had learnt the lesson well. He bowed his head in thanks and left Birbal's mansion.

Birbal's Curry

One evening, In the royal court Birbal said to King Akbar, "Your Majesty, I have been invited to dinner so I have to leave early."

King Akbar let him go early. Next day King Akbar enquired about the dinner. Birbal started listing the dishes that had been served at the feast. But, before he could complete the list, King started talking about the roses abloom in the royal garden. The discussion about the feast was left unfinished. Early next morning when Akbar asked Birbal, "And what else ..... ?"

Before he could complete the sentence, Birbal said, "Your Majesty, and curry."

King Akbar remembered that Birbal had said that word to complete the list of dishes served at the feast they were talking about yesterday. King Akbar was impressed by Birbal's memory and gave him his pearl necklace as a reward.

The courtiers, who were watching and hearing the conversation, did not understand a thing. They were confused why just saying "curry" had earned Birbal a reward. Some of them thought that curry must be King Akbar's favourite dish. They went home and asked their wives to prepare delicious curry.

Next morning all the courtiers entered the royal court with each having a servant carrying a covered vessel. As the King arrived and sat on the throne, the covered vessels were placed in

front of him. King Akbar grew confused. "What on earth do these vessels contain ?" he enquired.

One of the courtiers stood up and said, "Your Majesty, it seems curry is your favourite dish that is why you gave a handsome reward to Birbal yesterday. All of us have brought tasty curry for you. Please taste them so that you may reward the one who has brought the tastiest curry for you."

"How dare you make fun of me ?" King Akbar grew angry.

"You knew nothing about what we were talking about yesterday and why I gave that pearl necklace to Birbal. You made your own assumptions. You are fools with no brain to think. You merely copy others and feel jealous at other's success. I order all of you to be put in jail."

The courtiers apologised for their behaviour and the merciful King Akbar accepted their apology.

The Five Queries

One day King Akbar asked five questions to his courtiers.

The first question was- which flower is the best? No one replied for a while. Then one courtier named rose and the other said that it is the lotus.

The second question was- which milk is the best ? At this the courtiers argued that the goat's milk is the best, but others said that the cow's milk is supreme.

The third question was- which is the best of all sweetness? Some pointed it to be rasgulla and others listed other such sweets.

The fourth question was- which leaf is the best ? Some said tulsi and others said banana or neem.

The last question asked by King Akbar was- which is the best king of all ? To this all the courtiers agreed that King Akbar is the best king.

The last answer pleased King Akbar immensely but he was still not satisfied with the answers of the questions. Just then Birbal arrived in the court. King Akbar posed the same questions to Birbal. Birbal showed his usual intelligence and answered the questions differently.

"Your Majesty," Birbal said. "The best flower is that of the cotton plant. We get fibre from them to make clothes which cover our naked bodies. The best milk is that of a mother for it helps a baby grow into a healthy being. The best of all sweetness lies in our tongue. Whatever our tongue likes is sweet for us. The best leaf is that of betel as it is offered to all who are friends, foes, guests and relatives and leaves us feeling fresh."

Now King Akbar asked, "Who is the best king of all, Birbal ?"

To this, Birbal replied, "It is King Indra, Your Majesty. He is the God of Rain. If there is no rain, there will be no crops to feed us, to keep all living creatures alive. Crops, in turn, bring prosperity and wealth in our lives."

King Akbar was very pleased and satisfied by the answers he received from Birbal.

Abdul Karim's Right Eye

Birbal had a habit of chewing tobacco. Once as he was passing by the royal palace chewing some tobacco, he spat out. The spit left a mark on the palace wall. Abdul Karim, a jealous courtier was watching this. He was blind of one eye which gave him a sinister look.

Abdul Karim ran to King Akbar's chamber and complained, "Your Majesty, I saw Birbal spitting on a palace wall after chewing tobacco. Do you think it's right ?"

King Akbar grew furious when he heard it. He sent for Birbal. As soon as Birbal arrived, King Akbar said, "Birbal, you are an intelligent man. There is no harm in chewing tobacco. But you should spit it out in a vacant, useless spot."

Birbal apologised and promised to do so the next time round.

Next day Birbal arrived in the court. He was chewing tobacco. Abdul Karim kept watching him. He was sure that Birbal would spit on a wall in the royal court and he would then insult Birbal to his heart's content. But Birbal turned around and spat into Abdul Karim's right eye. Abdul Karim became furious. He screamed, "Your Majesty, look what Birbal has done. He has spat right into my eye."

"Birbal, why did you do that ?"

"Your Majesty, you had asked me to always spit in a vacant and useless spot. As Abdul Karim's right eye is blind, it is a vacant, useless spot. Isn't that so ?"

King Akbar burst out laughing. Abdul Karim understood that he had been given a fitting reply.

Birbal and the Hairless Palms

Once King Akbar was looking at his palms, he thought up a question. He sent for Birbal immediately. When Birbal came to King Akbar, He asked him, "Birbal, tell me why I don't have hair growing on the palms of my hands ?"

Birbal grew thoughtful and replied, "Your Majesty, your palms are always busy giving away alms and rewards to the people around you. As the palms are rubbed against all the time, no hair can grow there at all."

King Akbar smiled and then asked another question, "And why don't I see any hair growing on your palms, Birbal ?"

"Oh ! Your Majesty, you are too kind and giving. You are always giving me gifts and rewards. My hands are always busy receiving them so the rub on my palm does not let the hair grow there."

King Akbar laughed at Birbal's witty reply and rewarded him for his hairless palm once again.

Birbal once arrived in King Akbar's chamber carrying a heavy book. On enquiring, Birbal told the King that he is holding the Mahabharata, a holy book of the Hindus. King Akbar wished to read it so Birbal left the Mahabharata with the King.

A few days later King Akbar summoned Birbal and said, "Birbal, I want you to write an Akbari Mahabharata. You can take as much money as you want."

Birbal got worried at such a strange request which could not be fulfilled at all. But Birbal said, "Of course, Your Majesty ! It will be done. But I need two month's time and fifty thousand gold coins to spend on."

"I agree to your demands, Birbal." Birbal went home with a worried face. "Mahabharata is a holy book written by a great sage. How could Akbar's

Mahabharata be created ?" As he pondered he had an idea. He spent some money to buy a tonne of waste papers. Then he gave away the rest of the money to Brahmins and poor as alms. After resting well for two months, Birbal arrived in the royal court. On seeing him, King Akbar asked, "Birbal, I had asked you to write Mahabharata about my Mughal dynasty. What did you do about it ?"

"Your Majesty, your work is in progress. Ten Brahmins are busy writing it. If you can give me

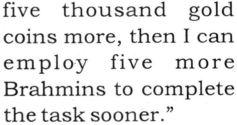

five thousand gold coins more, then I can employ five more Brahmins to complete the task sooner."

King Akbar agreed and Birbal took leave for another month. At the end of the month, Birbal made bundles of waste papers and bound them up as many heavy volumes of a book. He took all the volumes of the book to court. There he said to the King, "Your Majesty, I have the Akbari Mahabharata ready but before presenting its

volumes, I need permission to seek the Queen's advice."

With the King's permission, Birbal took the books to the Queen and said, "Her Majesty, His Majesty had ordered a royal Mahabharata to be written. I have got  it created by great learned persons and I have brought it with me to show you."

"Oh, that's a great thing, Birbal !" exclaimed the Queen.

"But, Her Majesty, there is a problem."

"Yes, tell me if I can help you," the Queen said.

"Her Majesty, you know that in the Mahabharata, Draupadi had five husbands. As you are one of the characters of the royal Mahabharata, so in the book you also have five husbands. And as you know Draupadi had been disrobed in the royal court by Dusshasana, so you as a character in this book are undergoing the same......"

"Keep shut, Birbal. How dare you say that ? I don't want to hear anything," the Queen grew angry.

"But, Her Majesty, the royal Mahabharata must be

much like the original...."

"No, I'll have none of this nonsense. Get me those silly volumes. I'll burn them to ashes."

Birbal had achieved just what he had wished for. The Queen got her maid to torch the volumes of the books Birbal had brought. Birbal slipped away and informed King Akbar about that. The King became very angry at the news. He rushed to the Queen's palace. By the time the King arrived there, the books rather the waste papers had turned to ashes. Being asked the reason to do so, Queen told King Akbar as to why she had torched the Akbari Mahabharata. On hearing the reason, King Akbar got alarmed. He promised the Queen that there would be no royal Mahabharata of the Mughal dynasty.

Later on Birbal confessed to all that what he had done with the waste papers and the money. King Akbar felt happy at Birbal's honesty and rewarded him for his wit.

The Art of Fortune-Telling

All the courtiers in King Akbar's royal court were very jealous of Birbal's favoured position. They were always trying to play tricks on him. One day they made a plan. In the court, one of them got up and said, "Your Majesty, I have observed that Birbal has not been paying attention to his work. He is engrossed in learning the art of fortune-telling and other related magics."

Another courtier said, "Your Majesty, we are fed up of listening to him bragging about his magical skills. He claims he can do anything by his magic mantras."

King Akbar grew thoughtful about testing Birbal to know the truth. When Birbal arrived in the court, King Akbar said, " Birbal I have heard that you have gained the knowledge of fortune-telling and magic mantras. Can you use your art for locating the ring that I lost a few minutes ago ?"

Birbal understood that the courtiers must have some plan to put him in place, so Birbal agreed and said, "Yes, Your Majesty. You will see that the ring will automatically reach to your finger." Birbal took a piece of paper and drew some abstract lines on it. Then he asked the King to place his hand on the paper. Then Birbal took some grains of rice and threw them on the courtiers. The courtiers started getting nervous. One of them thought "I must hold on to the ring in my pocket. Birbal had said that the ring would reach the King's fingers itself."

Thinking so, the courtier held his pocket tightly. Birbal noticed this. He said aloud, "Your Majesty, I have found the ring. It is in this courtier's pocket." At once all the courtiers knew that they had been tricked into this. King Akbar had himself given the ring to the courtier to hide but his nervous actions had given him away.

King Akbar realized that the courtiers had fallen into their own trap. He praised Birbal once more and gifted him the ring he had helped to locate.

The Stolen Bottle

Once due to very busy schedule in royal proceedings, King Akbar could not attend the royal court for many days. Sometimes when he felt very tired he would retire to his harem and share jokes with his wives.

One afternoon the King asked his wives, "Now each of you must tell me a silly tale. The one whose story is the most non-sensical will be rewarded."

Birbal was the only man who was allowed to enter the harem other than King Akbar himself. As he reached the doorway to the harem, he heard the King's strange words. He thought, "Surely there is something wrong. The King never misses attending the royal court and he never makes such silly requests. There must be something other than work that is keeping him away from the court. Perhaps he has started taking some intoxicating drugs that makes people act foolishly."

To find out Birbal made a plan. He did not go to the

royal court for nearly a week. Everyday King Akbar waited for Birbal but he never came. The King got worried. He thought that Birbal was ill. He decided to pay him a visit. As the royal entourage neared Birbal's house, his servants informed him. When the King arrived he was welcomed into the house by the servants. As instructed by Birbal, they told the King that their master was not at home yet they made the King sit. Soon Birbal's daughter arrived and offered refreshments to the King and his entourage.

As his daughter kept the King busy, Birbal slipped out of the backdoor. He went into the Queen's palace and in the chamber where King Akbar would rest near the harem. In the chamber Birbal saw a locked cupboard. He found the key on a nearby table. Birbal unlocked the cupboard. To his amazement he saw a variety of wines and drinks in the different bottles.

"Oh! the King has started taking drinks. Now I know why he behaves in silly ways sometimes."

Birbal picked a

bottle, locked the cupboard, put the key on the table and slipped out of the Queen's palace. Birbal wanted to reach home without being noticed but fate had something else planned for him. On the way home, Birbal came face to face with King Akbar. As soon as this happened, Birbal hid the bottle in his shawl.

"Birbal, what are you doing here and what's that you are hiding ?" Akbar enquired.

"It's nothing, Your Majesty, it's just a parrot." Birbal said.

"A parrot ! Are you joking ?"

"Oh, no, it's a horse I am hiding."

"Are you out of your mind, Birbal ?"

"I am sorry, Your Majesty, it's just an elephant ?"

"Have you taken some drugs ? You are talking nonsense."

"Your Majesty, actually my shawl is hiding a donkey."

"Birbal, that's enough now," King Akbar got angry.

At this, Birbal took out the bottle of wine. Seeing it

King Akbar asked Birbal to accompany him to the Queen's palace. There he opened the cupboard with drinks in it. By seeing a missing bottle, he at once came to know that Birbal had meddled there. So he said, "Are you drunk, Birbal ? You don't behave this way all the time. Today you gave me stupid answers all the time."

"No, Your Majesty, I've not drunk or had any drugs. I was merely telling you the effects of wine."

"And what are they ?"

"The first time I said, I had nothing in my shawl. It meant the first sip of wine takes away one's senses. When I said 'parrot', I meant that the second cup of wine makes a man speak on like a parrot. After the third cup he starts neighing like a horse as I had said. Then I had named an elephant. After drinking the fourth cup of wine a person starts walking like an elephant and the last time, I had mentioned a donkey. The last i.e. the fifth cup turns a man into a donkey for he acts foolishly."

King Akbar now realized his mistake. He at once threw away all wine bottles and gave up drinking.

The Angry Brahmin

A very learned Brahmin lived in Delhi. He was a regular visitor to the royal court. The King, Birbal and all the courtiers respected him as he gave good advice and told tales from the scriptures. But everyone was very afraid of his anger and stubborn nature. It was the Brahmin's nature that he would do or complete the task he made up his mind to do.

One afternoon he sat down for lunch. His wife served him the hot lunch. Just as the Brahmin took his first mouthful of rice, he spat it out. Picking out a hair out of the rice, he said, "There's a strand of hair in the rice. I do not like this at all. This is the first time this has happened so I'll forgive you. If it happens again then I'll not spare you."

With these words the Brahmin got up and walked out of the house. His wife felt sad that her husband had gone out hungry. She promised herself to be careful whenever she cooked. She would now tie up her hair well before cooking. But, as fate would have it, a few days later the Brahmin found a strand of hair in his food once again. He grew very angry and said "I had warned you. I won't take any of this. Now you'll suffer. I'll call the barber and shave your hair off."

Saying this, the angry Brahmin left the house to fetch the barber.

The Brahmin's wife got very scared indeed. She locked herself into the house. Soon enough her husband came back with the barber. He knocked at the door but his frightened wife did not open the door. The Brahmin shouted in anger, "Why don't you open the door ? I have fetched the barber. Now I'll teach you a lesson."

The Brahmin's wife was in tears. But she did not dare open the door. After waiting for a few minutes, the barber left the Brahmin's house promising to return soon. When constant threats did not make her open the door, the Brahmin yelled, "I am going to get the carpenter. He will cut down the door with his sharp saw."

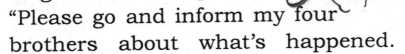

With these words, the Brahmin went away. After that his wife came out of the house and went to her neighbour and requested, "Please go and inform my four brothers about what's happened. They'll come to rescue me otherwise my husband will shave my hair off."

Then the Brahmin's wife returned and shut herself into the house again. The neighbour rode on horseback and went to the next village. He told the problem to the Brahmin's brothers-in-law. They soon accompanied him back to Delhi. On the way, one of them said, I'll go to Birbal for advice. He is my friend. You three go to help our sister."

As the others went off, the fourth brother went to met Birbal. After seeking Birbal's advice he, too went to his sister's house. A crowd had gathered there. The Brahmin was banging on the door to get his wife out. The fourth brother called the others and they went off for a while. They returned with shaved heads. They also had a white cloth used to cover dead bodies. Soon Birbal arrived there with some woods. They all made a pyre of the wood. Then they caught the Brahmin and wrapped him in the white cloth and made him lie on the pyre.

"What are you doing to me ? You are ridiculous to treat me as if I am a dead body !" exclaimed the Brahmin.

One of the brothers said, "Sir, you are a learned man. You know that according to Hindu customs, a Hindu woman's hair is shaved off only when she is widowed. If you wish your wife's hair to be shaved off then you must die."

The Brahmin was taken aback to hear this. His wife who was watching all this from the window, came running out of the house. "Oh brothers, why are you treating my husband this way ? Please spare him,"

By now the Brahmin had realized his mistake. He apologised to his wife and brothers-in-law. He thanked Birbal for helping him realize not to let anger rule our senses.

The Queen's Victory

One day King Akbar was relaxing in the harem with his Queen. He said, "I wonder what Birbal's brain is made of. He is always providing intelligent advice and witty answers. He is truly fit to be the part of the royal court's navratnas. In fact, he is the best of all."

At this the Queen burst out laughing.

"Why do you laugh this way, dear ?" King Akbar enquired.

"I can defeat Birbal in intelligence and wit," she claimed.

"Is that so ? I'll call him here and you'll have to prove it to me," the King said and the Queen readily agreed.

Soon Birbal was summoned to the harem by King Akbar. On his arrival, the Queen asked a maid to bring sharbat, fruits and sweets for Birbal. When she had left, the Queen waited for a minute or two and said, "Now the sharbat is being made. Now it has been poured in a silver cup. Fruits have been arranged in a bowl. The sweets have been placed in a silver plate. And now goes, one... two... three.... four... five... six... seven.... eight... nine... ten and Birbal, here is some refreshment for you."

As the Queen said this, the maid arrived with the refreshments at the chamber's door. The Queen turned to Birbal and said, "Did you see, Birbal, how I counted the minutes to the last ? And now let me inform you that the King and I will come for lunch to your mansion tomorrow."

"You are welcome, Her Majesty," Birbal said and left the harem.

Then King Akbar asked the Queen, "You were going to prove that you can defeat Birbal but I did not see any such thing."

"Your Majesty, the true test is to be held tomorrow at lunch."

The next day, the King and the Queen reached Birbal's

mansion. They were given a warm welcome and soon they had settled down.

"Birbal, I am sure that a grand lunch is being prepared for you. Now can you count and tell when the dishes will arrive as I had done yesterday?"

Birbal smiled humbly and said, "Your Majesty, I dare not speak before you. I request you to count and the minute you stop, the lunch would arrive."

The Queen agreed. She counted "one... two....... nine...... ten."

Just as she stopped at ten, five of Birbal's servants arrived there holding the dishes.

At this the King asked, "Dear, what do you say now?"

The Queen replied, "I think Birbal is more intelligent. He must have already guessed about

my challenging plan."

"Oh, yes! But that means dear that you've lost the bet of winning by challenging him."

"Yes, I do agree that he is very clever."

But Birbal said, "Your Majesty, in fact it's Her Majesty who has been victorious for the lunch arrived when she stopped counting as I had asked her to."

"Oh, Birbal" the Queen exclaimed with a laugh, "You are a rare one indeed. You made me win even though I had lost."

And the King laughed out loud at this.

The Trick of the Stick

On a fine evening King Akbar was enjoying a boat ride in a river. Birbal, some courtiers and guards were with him. As the boat moved on, King Akbar saw a small stick floating on the water surface. He said, "Whoever crosses this river just by using this stick floating in water will be made King for a day."

Saying this, he put his hand in water and picked up the stick. None of the courtiers were courageous enough to accept the challenge. King Akbar posed the same challenge to Birbal. Birbal agreed but said, "Your Majesty, I'll use nothing but this stick to reach the shore as you said but only after you declare that I am the King for the day starting from now itself."

"All right, I agree. Now my kingdom, treasures, guards and courtiers are yours for a day. You are now the Emperor of India."

Then Birbal bowed and took the stick in his hand. He was about to jump into the river but the courtiers called him, "Your Majesty, you cannot jump. We won't let you. You are our king. Who will take care of us if any harm comes to you?"

"No, it doesn't matter," Birbal said and holding the stick in his hand, he got ready to jump into the water again. But then the guards stopped him.

One of them said, "You are our king, we are your servants and we are faithful in your service. How can we let you be in any type of danger? It is our duty to protect you. We will not let you jump at all."

"Let me go, I order you," Birbal said forcibly.

"We are sorry, Your Majesty, but we cannot obey this order of yours."

The argument continued for about ten minutes but by then the boat has reached the shore. Then King Akbar said, "Dear Birbal, you have lost this time. You didn't use the stick to get across the river."

"I beg your pardon, Your Majesty, but I did use the stick. You had declared me to be the King for the day. But still I attemped to jump into the waters to swim across, using the stick. My dutiful guards prevented me from doing so. I kept holding on to the stick till we reached the shore. So you can say that I cross the river using the stick."

King Akbar realized that Birbal had indeed won again.

God's Justice

One fine day, during a conversation, King Akbar asked Birbal a question. He said, "Birbal, we all say that God is just and merciful. But I see that it is not true. In this world, we see so many different people. Some are very poor and others are wealthy. If God is our Father, we must all be treated equally by Him. Why does He show this prejudice ?"

Birbal grew thoughtful and then replied, "Your Majesty, if the God does not do this, no one would pray to Him. You are our King and like a father to all the people in the kingdom. You yourself employ many people and to some of them you give rewards at times. Some receive five gold coins, some a hundred and some thousands. Why do you do that ?"

King Akbar was perplexed at this question. He started thinking but did not get a suitable answer. Then Birbal continued, "Your Majesty, you pay your servants, or reward someone according to the work they do. One who works hard and long gets more than the one who does light work. Would it be right to call you unjust ? At times when someone does wrong, you deduct some money from the pay or scold him hard. If everyone was paid equally then no task would be done well. The God helps those who work hard and always pray to Him. He does not let troubles hurt them. Those who do not toil enough, are punished by Him. One gets the reward according to the work put in. One who works very hard eventually becomes rich and others stay as poor as they are. It is man's own doing and God can do nothing about it."

Hearing this, King Akbar understood the logic of Birbal's explanation. He thought deeply for a while. Then he praised Birbal for his clever answer.

Two Grateful Beings

King Akbar had the habit of placing challenges for Birbal. His witty solutions always amazed the King who appreciated Birbal's intelligence.

One day King Akbar made a strange request to Birbal. He said, "Birbal, I want you to get me two living beings. One must be a grateful one who is eveready to show his gratefulness and return it too, and second must be a person who takes the favours for granted and is never satisfied.

"Yes, Your Majesty. I will bring them with me tomorrow in the royal court."

Next day everyone in the royal court was curious to know who Birbal will bring. A little while later Birbal entered the court. He had a dog and his son-in-law with him. He bowed low to the King and said, "Your Majesty, here are the two beings you had asked for."

"Well, tell me about them, Birbal," said Akbar.

"This is my pet dog Sheru. He is a grateful being. I give him merely a small piece of bread everyday. In turn, he protects my house from burglars. He is always happy to see me when I return from work. Even if I do not feed him, he stays faithful to me as all dogs do. When people shoo away a dog after feeding once, the dog remembers this. A dog will be grateful for that one time and become a faithful friend. It will recognise you wherever you are and will come at one call of yours. He is eveready to return the favour and show his gratefulness."

"Go on, Birbal," said King Akbar.

"This is my son-in-law, Your Majesty. As all sons-in-law, he receives gifts and favours from me, 'the bride's father' all his life. A wealthy father may come down to the streets and empty all his treasures, but a son-in-law is never satisfied. He expects favours all the time. He is grateful for a moment but then takes it for granted. He thinks his position entails the gifts."

"You are quite correct, Birbal. I agree with you. Now I sentence this son-in-law to death for his ungratefulness."

Birbal got scared at the King's announcement. But as always, he used his wit and said. "Your Majesty, I was not talking about my son-in-law in particular. All sons-in-law are generally like this. Are you going to sentence all of them to death ? And Your Majesty, you must not forget that after all you are a son-in-law too."

Hearing this, King Akbar and all the courtiers burst into laughter. The King pardoned Birbal's son-in-law and was as always impressed by his witty minister once more.

Akbar's Half Brother

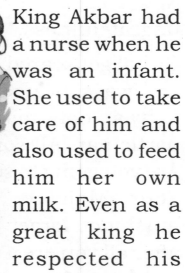

King Akbar had a nurse when he was an infant. She used to take care of him and also used to feed him her own milk. Even as a great king he respected his nurse who he called Dai Ma. Dai Ma also had a son. King Akbar considered him to be his half brother. He felt as they had been nursed by the same woman, who was a mother figure for him, so her son would be like a brother to him. Each time his half brother would come to meet the King, he would be welcomed with great lunch and many gifts. Many times the King would not even attend court as he was busy entertaining him. This habit used to irritate the courtiers and Birbal, too. They did not like the King's absence from the royal court for such a petty reason.

One day King Akbar asked Birbal, "Like my loving half brother, you, too, must be having one, Birbal."

"Yes, Your Majesty, I also have a half brother." "Well, why don't you bring him to the royal court? We would all like to meet him."

"But, Your Majesty, he is very young to come here."

"But you can surely bring him along."

Birbal agreed to the King's words. Next day everyone was shocked to see Birbal pulling a young calf into the royal court. The king was amazed too. He enquired, "Birbal, have you gone out of your mind ? Why have you brought this calf here ?"

"Your Majesty, I am merely following your order. Since I have been a baby, I have been fed on cow's milk. The cow is kept in our shed. As I have had her milk, she is like a mother to me. So her calf is considered my half brother. Isn't it so, Your Majesty ?"

King Akbar understood what Birbal was hinting at. He laughed out loud. Inspite of that, King Akbar never stopped loving and welcoming his half brother each time he visited the palace.

The Woman Cheat

Once a woman came in the royal court and said, "Your Majesty,

This man is a thief. He forcibly took off all my ornaments as I was passing by."

But the man protested, "No, Your Majesty, she is lying. I am a visitor to Delhi. This woman met me on a road and said that if I accompanied her she would let me meet you. I wanted to see you so I followed her. I have not taken away her ornaments as she is accusing."

But the woman started protesting loudly for justice and also started to cry. Birbal saw the King was confused. He thought of a plan. He asked the woman, "How much did your ornaments cost?"

"Five thousand gold coins, sir."

Birbal looked at the woman. She was a poor woman in dirty clothes. He was sure that she was lying. She could not have such valuable ornaments. Birbal called the servant and said, "Give her five thousand gold coins."

Later on, as the woman left the court with the money, Birbal called the man and advised him something into his ears. When the woman had gone out of the court, Birbal asked the man to do as he told him. As the man left, Birbal asked his servant to follow both the man and the woman.

The servant followed them. He saw the woman holding the money clutched in her hand and walking fast. Soon the man went to her and tried to

snatch away the money bag from her. But the woman held on tightly. The man tried hard but he could not get the bag from the clutches of the woman. But the man did not let her go with the bag of money and the woman was tired in fighting with man, she said, "You come with me to the royal court from where I got this money and I'll teach you a lesson."

The man and woman rushed back to King Akbar's

court once more. The servant ran to Birbal and reported all that he had seen. Soon the man and the woman entered the royal court. The woman said, "Your Majesty, this man did not let me go with my money bag. On the way, he followed me and tried again to snatch the money bag I had received".

Birbal intervened and asked the woman "Did the man try to snatch the bag from you?"

"Yes sir he pulled real hard but I did not let go."

Now Birbal grew very angry and scolded the woman, "You liar, if this man could not pull away a bag from your hands, how could he have forced you to give him the ornaments ? You lied before and falsely accused a visitor to our city. You will be punished."

Hearing this, she realized that she had been caught. She pleaded for mercy. King Akbar showed mercy and let her go, but she was not allowed to stay in Delhi. The visitor to Delhi thanked Birbal for his plan and went away happily.

Stay Within Your Limits

Many courtiers in Akbar's court were senior to Birbal. Yet when King Akbar showed his preference for Birbal, they felt very jealous indeed. One day all of them went to King Akbar's palace to talk about the matter. One of them said, "Your Majesty, we love and respect you as much as Birbal does and we have known you for many more years than he has. Why do you turn towards him for solving your problems ? Why do you never let us get a chance to win your favour."

King Akbar smiled thoughtfully. Then he said, "All right, today I'll see to your complaint. I'll pose you a challenge. If you are able to win it then you'll be given the place of honour that Birbal has."

The courtiers agreed. King Akbar ordered his guards to get a shawl of about two metres in length. Then King Akbar sent for a cot. He lay down on it and said, "Take this shawl. Each of you will get a chance to cover me with this shawl. The shawl must cover me in such a way that no part of my body stays uncovered."

King Akbar was a tall man. The courtiers tried hard to cover him with the two metres long shawl but no one got success. Some left the King's shoulder and arms uncovered while others left the legs exposed.

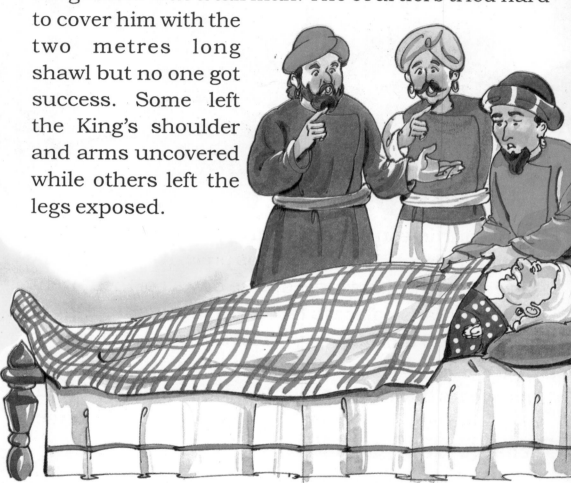

As this was going on, Birbal came there. On enquiring, King Akbar said, "Birbal, I'm here on the cot. I want them all to cover me with this shawl in such a way that no part of my body stays exposed."

Birbal approached the cot and said, "Your Majesty, I request you to bend your knees and curl up a bit."

As King Akbar did so, Birbal covered his curled up body with the shawl. King Akbar was completely covered with the shawl. Then Birbal said, "There is an old saying friends! It says,

"Stretch your legs as long as the shawl is." This means that one must stay within one's means or limits. If the shawl is small, you can bend a little to fit in. If your earnings are less, you can let go off luxuries and unnecessary things."

King Akbar got up from the cot. The courtiers had understood what Birbal had hinted at. They understood it that if they were not fit for the position, Birbal held, they would not get it.

King Akbar said, "Now you know that it is Birbal's wit and intelligence that has earned him this place and not my preference for him."

What I Desire

During the reign of King Akbar there lived a miser in Delhi. He was such a miser that he would only spend on what he needed to eat. The rest he used to shut away in a large box. He used to live in a small hut made of mud and straw. He did not even spend money on decent clothes. Seeing him, no one would believe that he had a large box full of gems and gold coins. He had kept the box hidden in a corner of his hut.

One day a fire broke out in his hut. The miser started crying and shouting for help. Hearing his cries, the neighbours gathered around to help. They brought buckets of water and tried their best to control the flames. But the straw hut showed no signs of stopping burning. As the miser started crying even louder, one of the men in the crowd asked, "Why are you crying so hard ? After all it is nothing but an old straw hut."

"Oh sir, you do not know. In the hut I have all my

life's savings. There are a lot of gems and gold coins in a box inside the hut."

The man who had enquired was a greedy goldsmith. He said, "I'll go in and get the box for you. But you must promise me that after getting the box, I will give you what I desire and the rest will all be mine."

The miser agreed. The greedy goldsmith jumped into the leaping flames to get the box. Soon he came out with minor burns and the miser's box.

The miser asked for his gems and gold coins. To this, the greedy goldsmith replied, "I had said that I will give you what I desire. Here I desire to give you this box and the gems and coins are all mine."

"Hey! But that's cheating. All right, I agree that you helped me out. You can take half of my savings and I'll

keep the other half."

But the goldsmith did not decline. As the argument continued, the miser and the goldsmith went to Birbal for justice. Birbal thought over the problem and said, "Goldsmith, you had promised to give the miser what you desire. Isn't it ?"

"Yes, sir, that is true," the goldsmith replied. "And what do you desire ?" Birbal asked. "The gems and coins, sir," pat came the goldsmith's reply.

"As per your promise, the gems and coins are the miser's as you had promised to give him what you desire."

The goldsmith realized that Birbal had played with his own words and there was nothing he could do about it. Thus the miser got his savings back due to Birbal's justice.

Mulla's Pagri

All time of the year, there were jealous courtier present in King Akbar's royal court. They were always making plans to demean Birbal. Sardar Mulla do Pyaja was a courtier who had won King Akbar's favours. He used to be very frank with the King.

One morning Birbal arrived in the court. King Akbar saw him and said, "Birbal, I like the manner you tie your pagri. It is tidy and tightly wound. It suits you well."

Birbal thanked the King for this. Hearing this, Mulla grew very jealous. He said, "What's so great about tying a pagri ? I can tie a better pagri than Birbal."

"All right," the King said. "Tomorrow I'll see how you tie a better pagri than Birbal."

The next day all the courtiers were surprised. The pagri that the Mulla had tied on his head was looking very good indeed. It was well-wound and tidy. Mulla was truly looking smart in it.

When King Akbar arrived in the court he, too, appreciated the pagri. He said, "Mulla, I agree that your pagri is much better than Birbal's. It is very tidy indeed."

But Birbal intervened and said, "Please wait, Your Majesty. I believe that the Mulla's pagri is better tied than mine but if the Mulla tied it himself, he must untie it in the court and then tie it again to show us how he did it."

Mulla untied his pagri and started winding it round his head. He tried his best to tie the pagri again but he could not tie it the way it was before, Seeing this the courtiers wondered what was wrong.

King Akbar and Birbal were watching all this. Birbal said, "Your Majesty, Mulla cannot tie, a better pagri than mine. Actually it was his wife who had tied his pagri

today. That's why it was so neat. So that is his wife who has won the challenge and not him."

To this King Akbar laughed out loudly. "Mulla, it is funny indeed. The problems you cannot solve, your wife does it for you."

Mulla felt ashamed to hear such a comment. He vowed never to challenge Birbal in any sphere ever again.

Company Matters

One evening as King Akbar and Birbal were enjoying a stroll in the royal garden, Birbal made some witty comment that King Akbar did not like. But Birbal did not notice this. He continued to poke fun at the King in indirect comments. After a while King Akbar could not contain his anger any longer. In a loud outburst he shouted at Birbal, "Birbal, how dare you say something like this in the King's honour ? I respect your intelligence so I favour you. But there are times, I have noticed that you do cross the limits. Lately I have seen you have become very rude indeed. Your language crosses the thin line between jokes and indecency."

Always at his witty self, Birbal solemnly bowed to King Akbar and said, "It is not my fault, Your Majesty. It is the matter of the company that I keep. Your companions do influence your behaviour."

Hearing this, King Akbar burst out laughing. He knew that Birbal spent most part of the day with the King himself. Thus, Birbal got away with wit once again.

Fine Weather

Once King Akbar posed a question to his courtiers,

"Tell me when is the weather at its finest."

The courtiers were eveready to please the King and earn a reward. One of them got up and said, "Your Majesty, the weather is at its best in the spring season. Light breezes blow, the colourful flowers sway along. The cool temperature pleases everyone."

"No, Your Majesty," another replied. "Winter is the best. We get so many vegetables to choose from and a variety of hot beverages. Groundnuts and warm blankets warm our hearts, too."

Another courtiers intervened. "It is the summer

that has the best weather. It is hot but there are cool wines and walks by the rivers to be enjoyed."

Now it was Birbal's turn to answer. He got up and said, "Your Majesty, the finest weather is that when a man is well fed. If a man is hungry, he won't enjoy the spring breeze, the cold will bite him and the heat will make him even more restless. But a well fed man will enjoy the monsoon showers, the summer breeze and the warm fires. A hungry stomach leaves the mind with nothing to think about but food."

King Akbar was once again won over by Birbal's clever reply.

The King Of Iran

Birbal was a very famous person in King Akbar's court. His tales of intelligence had spread far and wide. The King of Iran had also heard of him. Once he invited Birbal to his royal court. He wanted to test Birbal's intelligence on his own.

After travelling for some days Birbal reached the royal court of Iran. He was given a warm welcome. After rest and some refreshment, Birbal was taken to the king's palace. But when he entered the royal court, a strange scene met his eyes.

In the court, there were four men sitting on four

thrones. Each of them wore the same royal robes, identical crown and ornaments. All of them looked so alike that it was difficult to make out one from the other. Birbal got confused. He had never seen the King of Iran, so he did not know whom to greet. Birbal thought for a moment and came up with a clever plan. He merely stood still without a word and kept looking at all the four. After about five minutes, he went and bowed in front of one of the men and said, "Greetings to you, Your Majesty. I bring a message of goodwill and friendship from my King, Emperor Akbar of India."

The man got up and said, "Birbal, welcome to Iran. You are indeed clever but tell me how you identified me as the true King. After all we have never met before."

Birbal smiled and said, "Your Majesty, when I had stood still and not spoken up, the other three men did not know what to do. They kept glancing at you to know how you would react, so they could copy you. But you, being the King, kept looking straight ahead.

The King of Iran was very impressed by Birbal's reply. He had wanted to test Birbal himself and now truly believed that he was the best.

The Royal Insignia

King Akbar had the habit of roaming round his kingdom in disguise. He felt that this way he would know if anyone in his kingdom was in need so he could help him out. But Birbal did not like this habit at all.

As King Akbar was going out one evening to roam around in disguise of an old man, Birbal said, "Your Majesty, I do not like this habit. You are in a disguise. Someone may harm you thinking you to be a common man. Or if someone comes to know that you are the King and are unguarded, you may be attacked."

King Akbar did not pay attention to Birbal's words and left the palace anyway. As he reached a lonely street, he felt he was being followed. He turned and saw a man. But the man pretended that he was looking elsewhere. King Akbar in disguise approached him and said, "Who are you?"

"Wanderer," the man replied.

"What do you do for your living ?"

"Simply roam around from place to place."

"Where do you stay ?" the King enquired.

"Everywhere," pat came the reply.

King Akbar got irritated by the silly replies. In an angry tone he said, "How dare you speak this way ? Do you know who I am ? I am the Emperor of India. If you do not believe me take a look at this."

Saying this, King Akbar took out the only ring with the royal insignia that only a King could possess.

"Let me see that," the man said and took the ring from the king's hand. Putting it in his pocket, he started to run.

King Akbar panicked. He started shouting "Stop thief, he is running away."

Soon a crowd gathered there and started to chase the thief. They caught him soon. Then the man took out the royal ring and said, "How dare you believe a fool's words ? I am no thief. I am the Emperor of India, King

Akbar. If you have any doubts, you can see this royal ring I have."

The crowd believed the man for only the King could have the royal ring. They bowed low to him. When King Akbar saw this, he got very scared. He rushed back to the palace.

"Only Birbal knows that I am the King in disguise. I must take his help to recover the royal ring from the cheat."

As the King reached his chamber, he saw a small bag on his bed. He opened it. The royal ring was in it along with a letter. King Akbar was very happy to get the royal ring back. He opened the letter eagerly and started reading it. The letter said, " Your Majesty, I had warned you that your roaming around the kingdom without guards was not free of risk. You could have lost a lot more than your royal ring today."

There was no name at the end of the letter. But King Akbar understood all. He thought to himself, "It means that man was Birbal in disguise. He played this trick to make me realize my mistake. Now I understand what Birbal feared. From now on, I'll never go out on such rounds alone. I'll have guards in disguise to accompany me."

Blinds Who Can See

Once the Queen wanted to give alms to all the blinds. King Akbar wanted to be sure that none of the blinds were deprived of alms, so he ordered his men to make a list of blind people in his kingdom.

As per order, the list of the blind people was prepared. It was presented before the King. King Akbar went through the list and, while giving it to Birbal, he said, "Birbal, take this list of blinds in our kingdom. Call all of them and make good arrangements for their lunch."

Birbal saw the list and said, "Your Majesty, there are more blind people than the one listed here. In fact, the number of blinds is much more than the number of sighted people in our kingdom."

"What a silly thing to say, Birbal. If it is true, prove it to me," challenged Akbar and Birbal agreed.

The next day Birbal took the frame of an old cot. He started weaving its rope. He had a servant standing next to him. Birbal sat on the road and started to work. Soon a man came and exclaimed, "Birbal, what are you doing?"

Birbal said something to his servant. The servant made a note in a sheet of paper he held. A little later some more people gathered on the street.

"What is wrong with Birbal ?"

"Why is he doing this ?"

"What does he want to achieve?"

Each time someone made a comment. The servant would make a note. The whole day passed this way. By evening, King Akbar, too, heard of this. He went to Birbal to see for himself. "I don't understand what you are doing here."

The servant again made a note. Birbal stood up and greeted the King. He gave the list to the King to see. Birbal said, "Your Majesty, this is a list of three hundred blinds."

"But what's my name doing in the last ?" enquired Akbar.

"Your Majesty, you are also one of them. You were the last person to come and ask 'What are you doing ?' even though you could clearly see that I was weaving the cot."

King Akbar started laughing and said, "Yes Birbal, I agree the number of blinds in our kingdom is more than the sighted people."

The Tough Question

King Akbar's royal court had been adjourned. The courtiers and the King were about to leave. Just then a guard rushed in and said, "Your Majesty, a learned Pandit from South India has arrived just now. He is eager to meet you and Birbal Saheb immediately. He has come all the way to Agra for this specific purpose."

"It's not right to keep such a man waiting. Let him come into the royal court," the King ordered.

As the guard went to fetch the Pandit, King Akbar said, "Birbal, it's late and I am feeling tired. You must deal with the Pandit quickly." Birbal nodded.

103

When the Pandit arrived, greetings were exchanged. Then he addressed Birbal and said, "Birbal, I have heard of your intelligence. I want to test you. Tell me if I can ask you a hundred easy questions or one tough question ?" Birbal thought, "The King is tired and wants to rest. There is no time to answer a hundred questions." So Birbal said, "Panditji, just ask me a tough question."

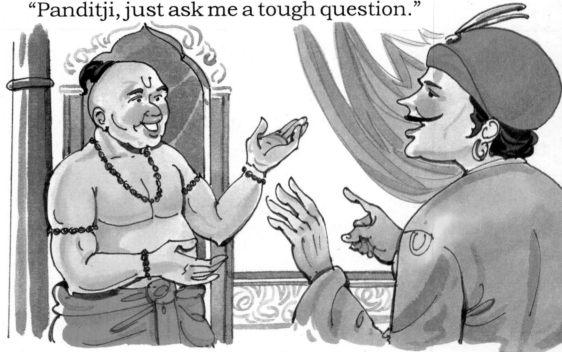

The Pandit asked, "Birbal, tell me which came first, the hen or the egg ?"
Birbal gave his instant reply, "The hen, Panditji ?"
"How can you say that Birbal ?"
"Oh no, no more quesions. Panditji you had promised to ask just a single question and your question has been asked," said Birbal.
The Pandit understood Birbal's cleverness. As he applauded Birbal, King Akbar and the courtiers, too, joined him.

The 'No' Day

Sultan Khan wanted to become an important courtier in King Akbar's court. When he heard that the royal treasurer had been dismissed, he decided to use his influence to place his son on the post. But Sultan Khan's son was a rogue. He was a cheat and a liar and tales of his misdoings were well-known.

From the next day Sultan Khan started taking his son to the royal court. He was on the look out to impress King Akbar. He was also very jealous of Birbal. Some days passed. One day Birbal had not arrived in the royal court. Sultan Khan saw a chance to turn the King against him. He got up and said, "Your Majesty, you can see that Birbal is not present here today. Now he has become careless about administrative matters."

King Akbar understood that Sultan Khan was trying to turn him against Birbal. He wanted to see what

Sultan Khan wanted to do. So he said, "Yes, Sultan Khan, I agree with you. What must I do to punish Birbal if he comes in late today?"

Sultan Khan felt glad at the King's words. He said, "Your Majesty, you must reply in 'No' for everything that Birbal says."

King Akbar agreed. When Birbal came in late, the King asked, "Birbal, why are you late today?"

"My wife is not well, Your Majesty. So I had to fetch the hakim. I got late due to this."

"No, I don't believe you," the King said.

"I am speaking the truth and I ask for your forgiveness," said Birbal.

"No, you'll not be forgiven," the King declared.

"Oh, it seems it's a 'No' day for the King today. He is

saying 'No' to everything," thought Birbal.

Just then Birbal saw Sultan Khan smiling at the King. He understood that he had been tricked. He also knew that Sultan Khan desired to get the post of the royal treasurer for his rogue son. So Birbal continued, "Your Majesty, at least let us discuss some administrative problems."

"No, there's no need for it," came the reply.

"Then may I please go home?" Birbal asked.

"No, I'll not allow you to go ?" the King replied.

Then Birbal said, "Your Majesty, may I request you to appoint Sultan Khan's son as the royal treasurer ?"

"No, Birbal, I'll not do it," King Akbar said. Then he understood what Sultan Khan had wanted and how Birbal had got rid of the problem.

Sultan Khan heard the King's reply and felt shocked. His plan had ruined. The 'No' day had been a real bad day for him.

The Corrupt Officer

One day the guards presented a man in King Akbar's court. One of the guards said, "Your Majesty, he is a man caught taking bribe."

"What was he working as ?" the King asked. "Your Majesty, he is the officer in charge of the granary."

"Put him in prison. I'll think of his punishment later on." Then Birbal said, "A corrupt man will take bribes whatever position he may hold."

A courtier got up and said, "I beg your pardon but I do not believe this. There are some jobs in which one cannot take any bribe at all."

"All right," said Birbal "I'll put this corrupt man to the job you suggest and we'll see what he does."

So the courtier said, "Give him the job of counting the waves in the river Yamuna. I am sure he can't take bribe in this task."

King Akbar and Birbal agreed. The corrupt man was called from the prison. He was told to sit by the river Yamuna the whole day and count its waves.

Some days passed. One day King Akbar asked, "Birbal, is there any complaint from the man whom we had punished for taking bribes ?"

The courtier intervened, "There is no news, Your Majesty, I told you he can't take bribes there."

To this, Birbal said, "We'll go there tomorrow morning and see for ourselves."

The next day at dawn, Birbal, the courtier and King Akbar disguised themselves as fishermen. They took a boat, a net and went out to the river Yamuna. They rowed nearer to the shore where the man was sitting with a pen and paper in his hands and was busy in noting something. As they neared him, he got up and shouted, "Hey, who are you ? What are you doing here ?"

"We are poor fishermen, sir. We are here to catch fish from the waters."

"Do you know you've interfered some work being done by royal orders ? I have been appointed to count waves in the river. Now you've come and disturbed me. You'll be punished for this."

"But sir, we are poor fishermen." "All right, you'll have to pay a fine of a hundred gold coins."

"Be kind sir. We don't have so much but......"

"You can give me fifty gold coins, can't you ?" the man said.

But one of the fishermen said angrily, "He's asking for a hundred and I'll give to him," saying this, he took off his disguise. He was King Akbar. The man stepped back in shock.

"I'll give you a hundred lashes on your back." the King said to the man. Then he said to Birbal," You were right, Birbal. A corrupt man will find ways to take bribe whatever job he is in."

The courtier did not have anything to say. The corrupt officer was given a hundred lashes and put in prison.

The Washerman and the Potter

One day a washerman's donkey got into the courtyard of a potter's house. Who had put out his pottery to dry in the sun. The donkey trampled on the pots and all of them broke. Just then the potter came out of the house. Seeing the washerman's donkey in the courtyard and his broken pots, he grew very angry.

Picking up a stout stick, he started beating the donkey. As the donkey brayed loudly in pain, the washerman, who lived just next door, came to the rescue of his donkey. "Hey! Why are you beating up my donkey?" he shouted.

"He broke all my pots. I'll not let him off without a punishment," the potter said.

"I'll pay for all the pots broken. Let's settle this. Why fight for such a matter?" the washerman said. He paid the potter's money and left with the donkey. But the potter was still angry. He wanted to teach a lesson to the washerman.

The next day he went to the royal court to meet King Akbar. There he said, "Your Majesty, my friend returned from Iran last evening. He told me that the Shah of Iran is very impressed by the country and people, where we live. But he said that Indian elephants are black and dirty. His army has white and clean elephants."

"So what should we do about it ?" the King enquired.

"Your Majesty, the Shah of Iran has a large group of washermen who wash the elephants twice a day."

Hearing this, King Akbar realized the potter was upto some mischief but he did not show it. He asked, "Ask all the washermen in the city to get together and wash our elephants daily."

"Your Majesty, there is no need to call all of them. The washerman who lives next door to me washes very cleanly. He is enough to scrub our elephants clean."

Now King Akbar was sure about the potter's plan

so he said to his guards, "Go and fetch him."

The washerman was called and asked to scrub the elephants clean. The washerman scrubbed some elephants the whole day but the elephants remained dark. In the evening, the tired washerman grew worried. He was afraid of the King's anger because the elephants were still dark. He had also understood that the potter had planned all this to teach him a lesson. The washerman rushed to Birbal's mansion to seek help. After meeting with Birbal, he went back home as a much relaxed man.

Next morning when King Akbar scolded the washerman for not having cleaned the elephants he said, "Your Majesty, if I could have a big pot to dip the elephant while scrubbing it, surely we'll have whiter elephants than the Shah of Iran has."

King Akbar knew that the washerman was getting back at the potter now. So he said, "Ask the potter to make a big pot to fit the elephant in for bathing."

The potter was ordered to make the pot. He took a

week to make it. Then he took the pot to the palace. But, just as the elephant put its foot in it the pot broke due to its weight. The King grew angry, "You've made a weak pot. Go and make a stronger pot again. I want it here in the morning."

The potter knew that he had been caught. He fell down at King Akbar's feet and confessed that he wanted to teach the washerman a lesson. Then the King asked the washerman, "How did you get the idea to get even with the potter this way ? I'll reward you for this excellent idea you had."

"Your Majesty, it's Birbal Saheb and not me who deserves the reward. He told me the plan when I went to him for help."

King Akbar called Birbal and commended him for helping the washerman.

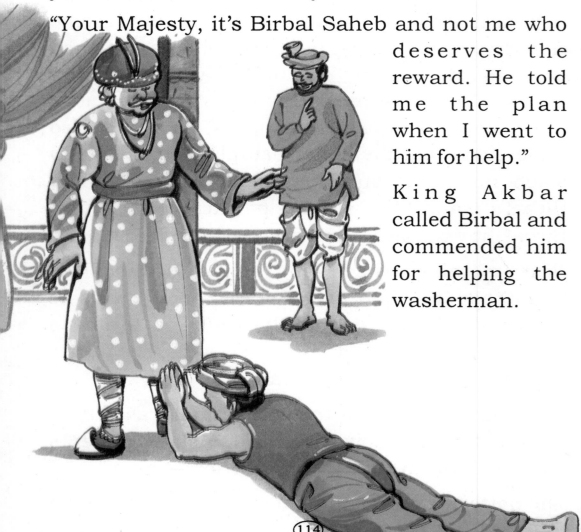

The Obedient Husband

One afternoon King Akbar and Birbal were roaming in the streets of Agra in disguise. Just then

they saw a woman shouting loudly. She was addressing a man. She was saying, "You are not fit to be a husband. Get out right now. Don't you dare step into the house without completing the task I gave you."

Seeing this, King Akbar asked Birbal, "Why is that young man not responding ? He is strong and he can shout back at his wife, too. Why doesn't he do anything ?"

"Your Majesty, all husbands are like this. They obey their wives. This is the bitter truth about marriage."

Next day King Akbar ordered all married men to come at the front of the palace. When the men had gathered, he said, "I want all husbands who obey their wives to step to my right, and those who don't, must step to my left."

At this order all the men stepped to the right of the King. Only one of them stepped to the left. King Akbar felt very happy thinking that atleast one of the married men was his own boss. He asked Birbal to reward him, but Birbal wanted to ask the man a question. He asked the man, "When all the men stepped to the right, you went the other way. Why did you do that ?"

"Sir, actually my wife has asked me to keep away from crowds so I decided to step away from these men."

Hearing this all the courtiers, the gathered husbands and King Akbar burst into laughter. The King turned to Birbal and said, "You were right once again, Birbal. You have proved what you had said. All husbands obey their wives."

Child's Play

"Why are you late today, Birbal?" King Akbar enquired one day as Birbal arrived late in the royal court.

"Your Majesty, I ... my son ...," Birbal faltered.

"Yes, go on, tell me what's wrong?" King Akbar insisted.

"I got late because my four year old son's toy broke. He did not let me leave the house till I mended it."

Hearing this, the King and all the courtiers burst out in laughter. Some commented, "Oh, Birbal got delayed by a child."

"The great Birbal could not make a child let him leave the house."

The King said, "Why Birbal, you are the most precious gem of my court. You help me get out of problems. Why couldn't you get out of a child's reach."

Birbal said, "Your Majesty, handling a small child is no child's play. A child can make a fool of a man. Even elders like us are no match to a stubborn child's wish."

"I don't believe it. Bring your son to the court tomorrow. I'll show you how to deal with him," the King said.

Next day Birbal arrived with his four year old son. After welcoming the child, King Akbar asked him, "Dear, what do you want? I'll get anything you desire."

"I want to eat a sugarcane," the child requested. "Get some sugarcane for the child," the King ordered. Soon the servants brought a plate in which peeled and cut pieces of a sugarcane had been served. The child saw them and said, "I don't want these. I want the whole sugarcane."

"Get another sugarcane for him and do not cut it this time." The King ordered his servant.

The order was followed.

"No..oo....o..oo..!" the child began to cry.

"What's wrong now dear'?" the King asked.

"I want this sugarcane to be put together again. I don't want the other one."

"No, dear, that's not possible. I'll get a long and sweet whole sugarcane for you," the King said

"No...o..o.., I want this to be joined back for me now," the child insisted and started crying very loudly. All the King's words fell on deaf ears. The courtiers and the King kept trying but the child kept to his request.

Then King Akbar threw up his hands and said, "All right Birbal, you win again. Now I understand that why even you could not satisfy a child. Fulfilling children's wishes is very difficult indeed."

The Most Beautiful

The courtiers in King Akbar's court were always making plans to remove Birbal from the favoured position he held. One day one of the courtiers went to Hussain Khan, King Akbar's brother-in-law and said, "You are the Queen's brother. Being the King's brother-in-law, you must hold the post that Birbal occupies."

"Oh, that's impossible. I can't do anything about it," said Hussain Khan helplessly.

"Why not ? Just ask your sister to put in a word for you. The King can never turn down the Queen's request."

Hussain Khan agreed. He went to the Queen and asked her to put in a word for him. That evening when King Akbar came to meet the Queen, she was not in a good mood.

King Akbar said, "Begum, something is surely bothering you. What's the matter ?"

The Queen said "I want my brother Hussain to get the

post that Birbal holds."

King Akbar said, "I can't give him that post, Begum. Hussain Khan is foolish and stubborn. One needs the intelligence of Birbal to help in royal administration. Further more I have no reason to dismiss Birbal."

The Queen said, "I have a plan. Tomorrow evening you must ask Birbal to fetch me in the royal garden for a stroll with you. I will refuse and when he won't be able to

persuade me then you can dismiss him in anger."

King Akbar agreed. The next evening he called Birbal into the garden and said, "Begum Sahiba is angry with me.

Can you go and ask her to join me for a stroll here? You must try to please her. If you don't bring her here then I'll dismiss you. I'll give your post to my brother-in-law, Hussain Khan."

Birbal realized that it was a plan to remove him. After making a plan, he went into the Queen's chamber and said, "Her Majesty, the King has asked you to join him for a ....."

As Birbal was speaking, a servant came and whispered something in his ears. The Queen could not hear all of it. She only heard three words - "The most beautiful ....."

Then Birbal turned to the Queen and said, "Sorry Your Majesty, the plan is changed now" and then Birbal took his leave.

The Queen got worried. She thought, "The servant said something about 'the most beautiful' and then Birbal stopped requesting me to go into the garden. Oh, my God, has the King found some beautiful woman for company ! Maybe that's why Birbal talked of a changed plan as I was not needed any longer."

Seething in jealousy, the Queen rushed to the royal garden. There she saw the King waiting for her all alone. Seeing her, King Akbar said, "Begum, you had said that you'll not heed Birbal's words. That's why you were not supposed to come here. Now you've lost the challenge. Tell me what made you come to the garden anyway ?"

The Queen had no answer to give. Clever Birbal had used his plan to secure his position once more. The Queen could not tell anything to the King out of embarrassment.

Most Loved Possession

Once, due to some mistake made by the Queen, King Akbar lost his temper. He scolded her and ordered. "I want you to leave the palace within twenty four hours. You may take your most loved possession if you want."

The Queen got very worried. She sent for Birbal to ask for help. Birbal told her a plan and left her chamber. Then the Queen asked her maids to pack all her belongings as quickly as possible. When everything was ready she asked her maid to call King Akbar. When he arrived, the Queen said, "As per your order, I am leaving the palace now. Can you share a glass of sharbat with me ?"

King Akbar agreed. The Queen poured him a glass of sharbat. After drinking the sharbat, the King felt very sleepy. He lay down on a bed and was soon in deep sleep. The Queen asked the guards to fetch a palanquin. The King was placed in it. Soon the Queen left the palace with her belongings. The guards carried the palanquin with the sleeping King and followed her to her father's house.

Soon the Queen reached her father's house. The King was placed on a bed. He was still sleeping. When the Queen's father asked what had happened, she told him to wait and see. In an hour or so the King awoke. He looked around. He saw the Queen standing by the window.

"What am I doing here ? How did I reach your father's house ?"

"Your Majesty, you had asked me to leave the

palace with my most loved possession. How can anything be more beloved for me than you ? So I brought you along."

Hearing the Queen's words, King Akbar smiled and said, "Oh, you are very clever dear to think of such a plan." "Oh no, Your Majesty," the Queen explained. "It was Birbal who told me to act this way."

"Oh, Birbal is behind all this. Well, let's go back to the palace and thank him." The King and the Queen went back to the palace and Birbal was rewarded for his clever plan.

Birbal in Burma

After failing once at getting Birbal's post, Hussain Khan tried to please the courtiers. He thought that they would help him.

One day a courtier said to King Akbar, "Your Majesty, We've had a Hindu minister for so long. We must give a Muslim the chance to become a minister. We suggest your brother-in-law Hussain Khan for the post."

King Akbar who treated all religions equally, grew angry, but he controlled himself. He said, "Before giving him the post, I want to get him some experience. Hussain Khan will go to Burma with Birbal. He must deliver this sealed letter to the King of Burma as soon as possible."

Next morning Hussain Khan and Birbal left for Burma. They reached the royal court and Birbal gave the letter to the King. On reading it, the King looked worried. He asked his guards to take both the Indian visitors to the guest palace and keep a watch on them. Birbal and Hussain Khan wondered why so many guards were

positioned around the guest palace. The same question bothered a Burmese mininster. He asked the King, "Your Majesty, why are our guests under such close guard ?"

To this, the King of Burma said, "The Emperor of India, King Akbar, has written that these two messengers must be hanged on full moon night. I wonder why he couldn't have them killed in India ? May be their important positions would have made the people angry at their execution. What if I kill them and King Akbar's successor attacks me in anger ?"

The Burmese minister went to Birbal and said, "Your King has ordered both of you to be hanged on full moon night."

Birbal had already felt that something was wrong so he had planned with Hussain Khan on 'how to behave'. So when the Burmese minister said this, Birbal said, "Please obey our King's order as per the letter."

"Yes, you must hang us according to orders," Hussain Khan repeated after Birbal.

The minister went and told the King of Burma about Birbal and Hussain Khan's behaviour. In the guest chamber, Birbal said to Hussain Khan, "If you want us to be saved then do as I say. When they take us for the hanging on the full moon night then insist to be hanged before me. I'll handle the rest, otherwise we will be killed."

Three days later Birbal and Hussain Khan were taken for the hanging. The moon was shining full and bright. Birbal said, "Your Majesty, my last wish is that I must be hanged first. As I gave you the letter first, please let me be hanged first. At this Hussain Khan insisted, "No, no, Your Majesty, I must be hanged first,

As I am the brother-in-law of the Emperor of India."

At this, the King of Burma asked Birbal, "Why do you want to die first ?"

To this Birbal replied, "Your Majesty, tonight

whosoever is hanged first, will become the King of Burma in the next birth."

The King of Burma thought, "I don't want anyone but my son to become the next King of Burma. I'll not let these men take away his right to the throne."

So the King of Burma asked his men to lead Birbal and Hussain Khan to the borders of his country. He gave them a lot of gifts for the Emperor of India. On their return, King Akbar asked Birbal, "How was your trip to Burma, Birbal ?" Birbal told the King all that had happened. King Akbar turned to Hussain Khan and asked him, "So Hussain Khan, can you now take over Birbal's post ?"

"No, Your Majesty," said Hussain Khan. "I cannot be fit for that post. Only an intelligent man like Birbal can hold this responsible job."

So Birbal reduced another name from his enemies list.

God's Justice

Birbal was one of the most important and intelligent of all the ministers in King Akbar's court. He was well known for his witty replies and clever solutions. King Akbar loved to pose difficult questions to Birbal but Birbal always got away with quick answers.

One day King Akbar was attending the royal court. He asked Birbal, "Tell me Birbal, when can we see God's justice ?"

Birbal thought for a while. All the courtiers and King Akbar waited for Birbal's answer. Then Birbal bowed to King Akbar and said, "Your Majesty, we can see God's justice when Your Majesty's justice is not in the right. Each time when you pronounce a wrong judgement, the God sees it and amends to declare His judgement."

King Akbar agreed. He remembered this and was always careful when settling cases so that injustice was done to none.

Fool and Learned

One day, after settling a case, King Akbar asked Birbal, "Birbal do you know the difference between a fool and a learned man ?"

"Yes Your Majesty, I know it," replied Birbal.

"Will you explain it in detail ?" asked King Akbar. Your Majesty, the person, who uses his brain in the most difficult and challenging situation without losing control, is a learned man. But the person, who handles the difficult situation in such a way to hamper the job or worsen the situation at hand, is a fool."

King Akbar had thought that Birbal would say that a literate person was learned but his clever answer strengthened Birbal's position in King Akbar's heart once again.

Birbal's Daughter

One day Birbal's daughter insisted on meeting King Akbar. She was a young girl of eleven years. She was also very intelligent and witty like her father. Birbal took her to the palace to please her. In the palace, she saw all the chambers and the royal gardens. Then she went to the royal court.

King Akbar was attending the royal court. He saw Birbal's daughter and welcomed her. After giving her some refreshments, King Akbar asked her, "Dear, do you know how to talk ?"

"Yes, Your Majesty, neither less nor more."

Hearing the answer King Akbar was confused "What do you mean by your answer, dear ?" King Akbar asked.

"I mean I talk less with elders and more with my friends."

Hearing her witty reply, King Akbar laughed and commented, "So you are, like father like daughter."

Swept Away

Once Birbal accompanied King Akbar on a visit to a village. The King wanted to learn if all the villagers were well or not. He wanted to find out who was needy. As they neared the village, they saw a man walking down the street.

King Akbar started to enquire, "What's your name ?"

"Jamuna," came the reply.

"What's your brother's name ?"

"Narmada."

"What's your mother called ?"

"Saraswati."

"What do you call your wife ?"

"Ganga."

Birbal could not control himself.

He said, "Please stop right there. Any more rivers you mention, we will be swept away. Wait till I arrange for a boat to row across."

Hearing this, the villager and King Akbar could not stop laughing.

Eight Feet Away

One day Birbal sat in the royal court. King Akbar was in a jovial mood. So he decided to tease Birbal to pass time. He knew that Birbal's reply will surely entertain him, so King Akbar asked Birbal, "Birbal, tell me the difference between you and a donkey ?"

Birbal looked at the King and then he looked at the floor. He seem to be calculating something. A while later, Birbal bowed to the King and made his witty comment, "Your Majesty, the difference is about eight feet of distance ?"

King Akbar realized what Birbal had done. In his jolly wit he had called the King a donkey.

The Most Learned Person

Once King Akbar asked Birbal to fetch the most learned person in the royal court. To this Birbal replied, "As you wish, Your Majesty. But for this task, I need seven days time and five hundred gold coins."

King Akbar agreed for that. Birbal took the gold coins and distributed amongst the poor and needy. After that he just stayed at home and relaxed. Then he went to a shepherd's hut. He took the shepherd's son, gave him a bath and dressed him up in neat and tidy clothes. He took him to the

royal court. On the way, he explained to him all that he was to do in the royal court. On reaching the royal court Birbal said, "Your Majesty, this is the most learned person I have found." King Akbar decided to test the boy, so he asked, "Where do you live ? What does your father call you ? What special quality do

you have ?"

But minutes ticked by and the boy did not answer. The King asked again, "Boy, are you deaf and dumb ? Why don't you answer me ?" At this Birbal said, "Your Majesty, he is learned and is showing his wisdom. He has learnt from his elders not to talk before the King and a more wise person than himself. He knows it's best to keep silent. He is merely following what he has learnt."

King Akbar was impressed. He gave many gifts to the shepherd boy and sent him away.

The Best Weapon

Once there was a discussion going on in King Akbar's court. King Akbar wanted to know which was the best weapon to be used for protection.

Some courtiers named the sword, some said the knife and others named the spear. Then King Akbar asked the same to Birbal. Birbal replied, "Your Majesty, if there was a best weapon then everyone would be using the same weapon. I believe that the weapon that comes in hands in a dangerous situation is the best weapon."

King Akbar said, "I don't agree with you at all."

Birbal decided to prove this to the King. The next day Birbal had already made preparations to prove his point. As he and King Akbar were walking through the city, Birbal directed the King through a very narrow street. As they walked, suddenly the King saw a mad elephant rushing towards them. As the elephant came nearer, the King panicked. He started to take out his sword but he knew that

the sword was not enough to stop the raging elephant. There was no time to run back through the narrow street. Just then Birbal saw a pup lying by a wall. He picked the pup and threw at the elephant. The pup was scared at being thrown this way. As it landed on the elephant's trunk, it held on tightly to avoid falling. As its teeth and claws clung tighter, the elephant panicked. He started walking backwards to get rid of the pup. He could not swing his trunk in the narrow street. As the elephant stepped back, King Akbar wiped the sweat from his forehead. He heaved a sigh of relief. Then Birbal said, "Your Majesty, in this situation the young pup was the handy and protective weapon to save ourselves. Do you think that the pup is a weapon ? Now do you understand what I was saying ?"

King Akbar realized and gave his pearl necklace as a reward to Birbal for saving his life and teaching him the lesson about weapons.

Emperor Forever

One day during a conversation King Akbar sighed and said, "Ahh ! If only there was a rule that once a person becomes an Emperor, he would rule his kingdom forever. Wouldn't it be bliss, Birbal ?"

Birbal waited just a second before retorting. "Yes Your Majesty, it would be indeed but then you would not be a King today."

"How is that, Birbal ?" King Akbar enquired. Birbal replied "Your Majesty, if your ancestors had not died and had been emperors forever then you would never have got the chance to rule."

King Akbar realized Birbal's logic and applauded him once again.

The Ever Moving

As always King posed a challenging question to test Birbal's intelligence. He asked his courtiers to answer a question. The question was, "What is the ever moving thing ?" Hearing the question, one courtier said, "Your Majesty, it's the sun."

"No, it's the moon, Your Majesty," another replied.

"It's our planet, the Earth, which is always on the move."

But all these answers could not please King Akbar. He had not got a truly intelligent answer yet. So he turned to Birbal and posed the same question to him. As an answer, Birbal said, "Your Majesty, it's the interest on the money that we take from a moneylender. The amount of interest keeps moving without fail and never gets tired. This goes on till we pay back, so it seems ever moving to us."

Now King Akbar was fully satisfied with Birbal's answer.

Whitest and Brightest

Once during a discussion in the royal court of King Akbar it could not be decided as to which thing in the world is the whitest and brightest. Some courtiers named cotton, others said that milk was the brightest. A courtier named snow to be the whitest and brightest of all. But Birbal remained silent. At this King Akbar enquired, "Why, Birbal, which do you think is the whitest and brightest of all ?"

'It's sunlight Your Majesty."

"Well, you'll have to prove it to me."

Birbal agreed to prove his words. Next afternoon it was very hot. King Akbar entered his chamber to rest. He ordered all doors, windows and curtains to be pulled close to keep light out. The dark room felt really cool to sleep in. In the evening when King Akbar awoke, he went towards the closed door. He tripped on a vessel which had milk in it. The milk soon spread on the floor. King Akbar opened the door and sunlight lit up the doorway. The King saw that some cotton puffs were also lying on the floor. Just then Birbal came to the door. King Akbar asked him, "Birbal, who placed this milk vessel and cotton near the doorway ?"

"I did Your Majesty," came Birbal's reply.

"Why did you do this ?"

"Merely to prove my point. If milk is the whitest then why couldn't you see it in the dark ? Why did you not see the bright cotton kept here ? Only when you let the door open and sunlight came in, then you could see. Thus, you now know that sunlight is the whitest and brightest of all."

King Akbar agreed with Birbal who had proved his point cleverly.

Akbar's Disguise

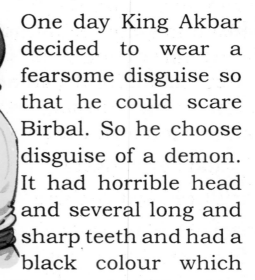

One day King Akbar decided to wear a fearsome disguise so that he could scare Birbal. So he choose disguise of a demon. It had horrible head and several long and sharp teeth and had a black colour which truly scared a person off. Wearing this disguise, King Akbar made a surprise visit at Birbal's mansion. But Birbal was very clever. He recognised King Akbar in disguise immediately. He welcomed him inside and felt very happy. After giving some refreshments to the King, Birbal grew thoughtful. Seeing this, King Akbar questioned, "Birbal, I see you were very happy but suddenly you are looking worried and deep in thought. What's the matter?"

"Your Majesty, you are quite right. I was very happy to receive you as a guest. But now I am worried. I can't make out what made you choose a disguise. Whom are you so scared of that you had to use a disguise to hide yourself?"

King Akbar felt ashamed that he could not scare even Birbal, instead he thought that the King was scared of someone.

Obedient Birbal

Birbal was a loyal and obedient minister in the court of King Akbar.

One day King Akbar's most loved Queen asked for him. As King Akbar was in the royal court, a servant brought the message there. The King thought of completing the work and going. A few minutes later, another message came asking the King to meet the Queen urgently. As the King loved his Queen very much, he got up to leave the court. Seeing his eagerness to leave the court, Birbal could not suppress his smile. King Akbar saw Birbal smiling and got angry.

"How dare you make fun of me ? You'll be punished for your insulting behaviour. I order you never to keep your foot on this ground ever. Just go away from here."

Birbal left the royal court. For many weeks he did not come to the court. Many courtiers, who admired him were missing him. Others, who were jealous of him, were happy at his absence. King Akbar was also worried. He was finding it difficult to solve many cases without Birbal's intelligent advice.

One evening King Akbar was looking out of the palace window. Suddenly he spotted Birbal going in a small chariot. He sent his guards to call Birbal. When Birbal presented himself before him, King Akbar asked, "Why are you not obeying my orders?"

"I was merely obeying your order, Your Majesty. You had asked me not to step on this ground as this ground is of your kingdom and the soil on it is yours, too. I had no choice. I went to the next kingdom and brought some soil from that kingdom. In this chariot I have spread that kingdom's soil, where I rest my feet. Now I am not stepping on your ground. Now I will spend my whole life on this small chariot."

Birbal's witty reply got King Akbar's heart and he forgave Birbal.

Printed at : HAPLOOS New Delhi Ph. : 549 868